DESERT NIGHT SHIFT
A Pack Rat Story

by Conrad J. Storad   illustrated by Nathaniel P. Jensen

Bobolink Media, Inc. • Fallbrook, CA

To Anna Storad, my Grams.
Thanks for teaching me the value of hard work.
– *Conrad, your oldest grandson*

To my big brother Allen Jensen and his incredible family:
Jenny, Joshua, Ashley and Benjamin, and to my mother-in-law Sandy Scholte.
Thank you all for your inspiration and support.
– N.J.

The illustrations were rendered in watercolor on Arches paper.
The text type was set in Goudy Old Style. The display type was set in Rosemary.
Composed in the United States of America. Graphic layout by Adriana Patricia De La Roche.
Production supervision by Laura Bofinger.

Printed in Singapore

First impression

Library of Congress Control Number: 2006904673

International Standard Book Number: ISBN: 978-1-891795-32-9 —Softcover

www.bobolinkmedia.com

12 11 10 9 8 7 6 5 4 3 2 1 (sc)

Oh, desert days are bright and hot,
Swift, hungry creatures rule,
But every little pack rat learns
That night shift work is cool!

The great Sonoran Desert
Is always dry and hot.
The place is harsh and rugged –
It's a very special spot.

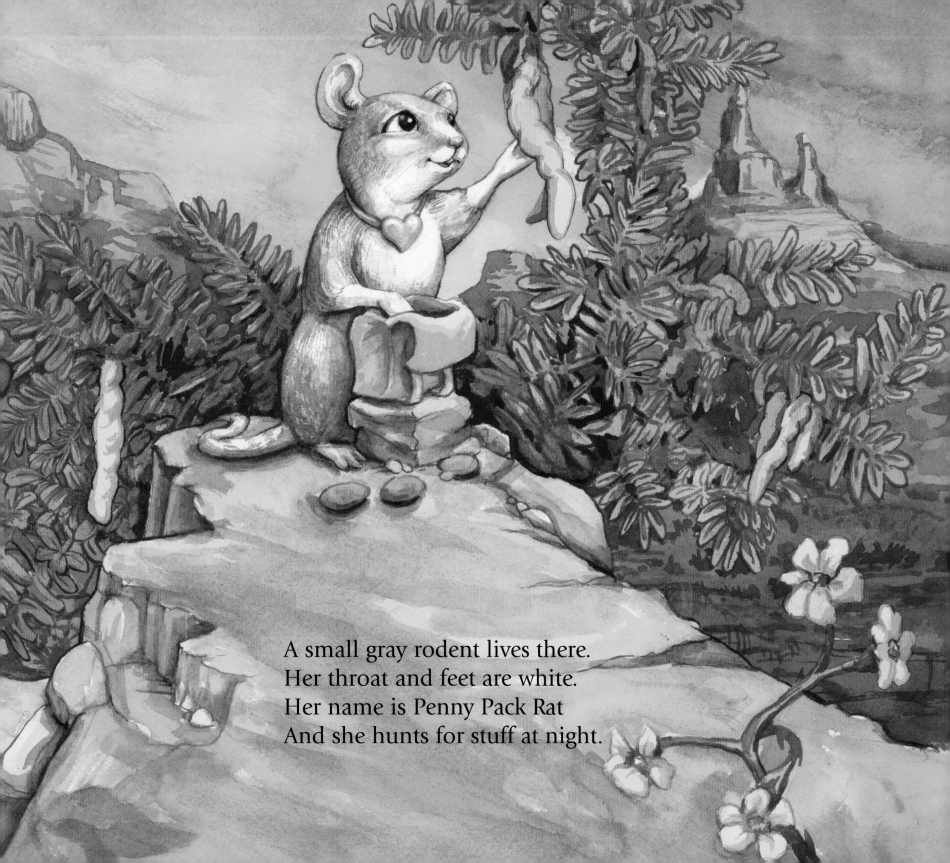

A small gray rodent lives there.
Her throat and feet are white.
Her name is Penny Pack Rat
And she hunts for stuff at night.

Penny really likes her name –
She knows it suits her best,
Because of seven copper coins
Stashed deep inside her nest.

Her house looks like a pile of trash.
The snakes stay far away.
The prickly sticky cactus spines
Keep predators at bay.

In one of Penny's many rooms
Mesquite seeds pile up deep.
Another room holds shiny things –
A third, soft grass for sleep.

There are nails and keys and bottle caps,
A watch that keeps no time –
A gold doubloon is lying there
Beside a shiny dime.

Now Penny's nana told her tales,
Some stories, very old,
How through the years the family
Found watches, coins, and gold.

"Great-grandpa found a watch," she said.
"Great-granny a doubloon –
But what I've always wanted
Is a shiny, silver spoon."

Penny shared this with her friends.
She told the Ring-Tailed Cat,
"I want to find a silver spoon
For Nana – she'll love that!"

Her treasure room was stacked with stuff
All lighted by the moon,
But nowhere in the pile of loot
Was there a silver spoon.

Oh, desert days are bright and hot,
Swift, hungry creatures rule,
But every little pack rat learns
That night shift work is cool!

Now when the moon had risen high
And the scorching day was done,
Penny knew she had to look –
Night was her time to run.

Night was when she gathered grass
And cactus chunks, and seeds.
And night was when she looked for things –
The treasures that she needs.

But night shift had its dangers, too –
Snakes and coyotes need to eat!
If they caught the little pack rat
She would make a tasty treat.

Penny's friends all wished her luck
When she went out this night.
The Elf Owl hooted, "Look out, yooo!
Those snakes can be a fright!"

The Deer Mouse and the Ring-Tail said,
"Our fear for you is real."
But Penny said, "Don't be afraid –
I'm not their midnight meal!"

Oh, desert days are bright and hot,
Swift, hungry creatures rule,
But every little pack rat learns
That night shift work is cool!

Penny tried the miner's camp
For metal, cans and trash.
"Perhaps this is my lucky night
For adding to my stash."

The miner's camp was dangerous.
The coyotes roamed that space.
But junk piles there were tempting –
It was Penny's special place.

Her silky whiskers wiggled
As she sniffed a pair of socks.
She saw three red, round bottle caps
Piled up beside some rocks.

Just then she heard the coyotes howl.
She had to choose – and fast!
She ran to grab a bottle cap,
Her good luck might not last!

And then as she was on her way
She saw it, near a can.
Something sparkled in the dirt –
She grabbed the spoon and ran!

Penny Pack Rat raced for home.
The coyote pack was near.
She stayed in shadows as she ran.
She zigged and zagged – no fear!

She made it home and waiting there
Was Nana at the door.
"This spoon's for you," said Penny.
"And tomorrow I'll find more."

The desert morn was dawning fast
So Penny went to sleep.
She drifted off and dreamed about
That promise she would keep.

Oh, desert days are bright and hot,
Swift, hungry creatures rule.
Now even Penny Pack Rat knows
That night shift work is cool!

Some Words to Learn

burrow **(BUR-oh)** – A hole or tunnel in the ground dug by a pack rat or other animal for use as home, nest, or shelter.

cholla **(CHOY-a)** – A common cactus that grows in the deserts of the southwestern United States and Mexico. The stem is made of sections that look like chunks of sausage covered with long, sharp spines.

forage **(FOR-edge)** – To roam around an area searching for something, usually food or building materials.

midden **(MID-en)** – A pile of trash or large heap of assorted objects. A pack rat's nest often looks like a mixed up pile of junk. Year after year, new pack rats add more items to the pile. The midden gets larger and larger.

nocturnal **(nok-TURN-l)** – Active at night. In the desert, pack rats and other animals often rest during the day to avoid the bright sun and hot temperatures. They search for food and are most active after the sun sets.

predator **(PRED-a-tohr)** – An animal that hunts and eats other animals.

White-Throated Wood Rat
(Neotoma albigula)

Size:	*Head and body 7 to 9 inches long; tail, 5 to 8 inches long; weight, 4 to 10 ounces*
Diet:	*Pulpy flesh inside joints of cholla cactus, mesquite beans, seeds, various grasses, and shrubs. Also eats the bark of smaller branches of mesquite and palo verde trees. In the hot desert summer, the wood rat eats food loaded with moisture. The tender young pads of prickly pear cactus is a favorite choice.*
Color:	*Body is gray, with a white or gray belly. Feet are white. Throat is pure white from base of hairs. Tail is white below, brown above.*
Range:	*Upper and lower Sonoran desert zones of Arizona, New Mexico, and northern Mexico*
Predators:	*Coyote, fox, bobcat, rattlesnakes, horned owl, hawks*

Scientists who study animals say that there are more than 20 kinds of wood rats living in North America. In this book, Penny the Pack Rat is modeled after the white-throated wood rat, often called a desert pack rat.

When the sun goes down at the end of the day, the Sonoran Desert comes to life. Many desert animals are nocturnal. They rest during the day to stay out of the scorching desert sun. The pack rat is one animal that likes to work at night. It roams across the desert floor searching for food as well as for twigs, sticks, rocks, and other material to build its nest. Pack rats forage in old trash dumps and search through camp-sites. They will grab a fork or spoon or anything shiny they find lying out in the open, then leave behind whatever else they were carrying. A trade is made. In the morning, a camper might find a twig or a seed where his knife or fork had been sitting. That's why pack rats are also called trade rats.

In the city, house rats have tails that are smooth and scaly. Desert pack rats have long, hairy tails. The pack rat's entire body is covered with fine, soft fur. It has long, silky whiskers and large ears. With its large brown eyes, the pack rat looks a little like a bunny rabbit.

The pack rat's nest is sometimes called a den or midden. Desert pack rats like to build their nest right in the middle of a prickly pear

cactus plant. They build underground burrows that they cover with mounds of sticks, twigs, and old cans. Inside, the rooms are lined with soft grass or plant fibers. Pack rats use prickly pear pads, pieces of cow dung, and the sausage-like sections of spiny cholla cactus as building material. The sharp spines on the pieces of cactus work like barbed wire to protect the nest from predators.

Paths called "runaways" lead into and out of the midden. These paths are also lined with sharp cactus chunks. A coyote or a fox will think twice before it tries to dig a pack rat out of its spiny home. A well-built midden provides security for many generations of pack rats. Some middens have been known to last for hundreds and even thousands of years.

MONSTERS OF THE DEEP

A FIREFLY BOOK

Published by Firefly Books Ltd. 2014

First printing

Publisher Cataloging-in-Publication Data (U.S.)

De la Bédoyère, Camilla.
Monsters of the deep / Camilla de la Bédoyère.
[80] pages : col. ill. ; cm.
Includes index.
Summary: A collection of animals from the darkest depths of the oceans.
Drawings highlight the extraordinary features of each animal's anatomy.
ISBN-13: 978-1-77085-465-9 (pbk.)
1. Deep-sea animals – Juvenile literature. I. Title.
591.77 dc 23 QL125.5D343 2014

Library and Archives Canada Cataloguing in Publication

De la Bédoyère, Camilla, author
Monsters of the deep / Camilla de la Bédoyère.
Includes index.
ISBN 978-1-77085-465-9 (bound)
1. Deep-sea animals—Juvenile literature. I. Title.
QL125.5.D43 2014   j591.77   C2014-901596-8

Published in the United States by
Firefly Books (U.S.) Inc.
P.O. Box 1338, Ellicott Station
Buffalo, New York 14205

Published in Canada by
Firefly Books Ltd.
50 Staples Avenue, Unit 1
Richmond Hill, Ontario L4B 0A7

Printed in China by 1010 International Ltd

Conceived, designed, and produced by
Marshall Editions
A division of the Quarto Group
The Old Brewery, 6 Blundell Street
London, N7 9BH UK

Editors: Emma Marriot and Jon Richards
Designers: Malcolm Parchment,
Marissa Renzullo, and Siân Willams
Art Director: Susi Martin
Publisher: Zeta Jones

MONSTERS OF THE DEEP

CAMILLA DE LA BÉDOYÈRE

FIREFLY BOOKS

CONTENTS

CONTENTS

LIFE AT SEA

Plankton
*up to 325 feet
(100 m)*

**Japanese
spider crab**
*up to 1,950 feet
(600 m)*

Our oceans and seas are home to many animals—from creatures that are too small to see to the world's biggest animal. We have found tens of thousands of species of ocean animals, but there may thousands more waiting to be discovered.

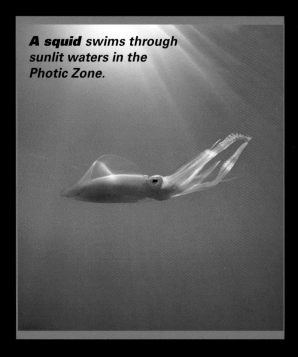

*A **squid** swims through sunlit waters in the Photic Zone.*

⊕ GIANTS OF THE DEEP

The largest animal that has ever lived on Earth is the blue whale. Even a baby blue whale weighs more than an elephant! Ocean animals can grow big, because the water supports their bulky bodies, allowing them to move and feed freely and without being crushed by their own mass.

PHOTIC ZONE

Sunlight passes through the Photic Zone, which descends to about 650 feet (200 m). However, the water quickly absorbs different colors of light the lower you go, including red, yellow, and orange light. Only blue light is able to reach the lowest parts of the Photic Zone. Below this is the Aphotic Zone, which is completely dark.

***Submersibles** are built to survive the huge pressures deep beneath the surface.*

PHOTIC

Blue whale
up to 650 feet
(200 m)

Sail fish
up to 650
feet (200 m)

Weddell seal
up to 2,400 feet
(740 m)

Firefly squid
up to 1,300 feet
(400 m)

**3,250 FEET
(1,000 м)**

Hatchetfish
up to 3,250 feet
(1,000 m)

Leatherback turtle
up to 3,900 feet
(1,200 m)

Great white shark
up to 6,175 feet
(1,900 m)

Snipe eel
up to 5,850 feet
(1,800 m)

Dragonfish
up to 5,850 feet
(1,800 m)

**6,500 FEET
(2,000 м)**

APHOTIC

Deep-sea angler
up to 6,500 feet
(2,000 m)

Sperm whale
up to 9,750 feet
(3,000 m)

Ratfish
up to 9,750 feet
(3,000 m)

**9,750 FEET
(3,000 м)**

SUBMERSIBLE

Submersibles are vessels
that travel deep underwater.
Scientists use them to find out
more about the ocean and the
animals that live in it. These
underwater craft are fitted with
powerful lights to see in the inky
darkness, and robotic arms to
collect sample specimens.

Flashlight fish
up to 13,000 feet
(4,000 m)

Starfish
up to 19,500 feet
(6,000 m)

**13,000 FEET
(4,000 м)**

Comb jelly up
to 22,750 feet
(7,000 m)

BLUE WHALE

The mighty blue whale makes massive journeys across the world's oceans, in search of food and a safe place to reproduce. This is the largest animal alive today—and probably the largest animal that has ever lived on Earth.

Blubber
Underneath the whale's skin is a thick layer of blubber—this is fat which the whale uses for energy.

BLUE WHALE
BALAENOPTERA MUSCULUS

DEPTH

0 feet
(0 m)

650 feet
(200 m)

SIZE • 85 FT (26 M)

	15 feet (5 m)	30 feet (10 m)	45 feet (15 m)	60 feet (20 m)	75 feet (25 m)

THROAT GROOVES
When a blue whale gulps in water to filter out tiny krill, grooves allow the whale to expand its throat up to five times its normal size.

The flukes are the large horizontal parts of a whale's tail.

FLUKE

When a blue whale dives it does a "headstand." Its tail, which has huge horizontal flukes, rises above the water, and pushes the animal down to depths of nearly 650 feet (200 m).

Small dorsal fin

Long, narrow
A blue whale uses
to change directi
it sv

On the surface, whales blow out a plume of water while breathing.

GIANT OF THE DEEP

Blue whales are up to 85 feet (26 m) long and weigh up to 120 tons. That's the same weight as 24 elephants! Their hearts are the size of a small car and their tongues are bigger than a hippopotamus. To fuel this huge mass, an adult blue whale will eat about 3.5 tons of krill every day.

BLOWHOLES

Blue whales breathe in air, not water. They have two blowholes on the top of their heads, which they use to breathe when they surface.

ALEEN WHALES

t baleen whales are huge, but they feed on tiny sea
als. Blue whales, grey whales, and humpbacks are all
en whales. They have special feeding structures in
mouths which they use to capture
l animals, but they need to eat
ns of them to survive.

Markings
*white patches are
t on every animal.*

HUMPBACK WHALES

Humpbacks are clever animals that often live in
family groups, called pods. They are also acrobatic,
despite weighing as much as 400 men, and often
leap out of the water in powerful breaching displays.

*An Antarctic dwarf minke
spy hops above ice floes in
the Southern Ocean.*

SPY HOPPING

A whale will sometimes pop
its head above the water to
look around. This action is
called spy hopping and some
whales hold this position for a
minute or more.

Long body
A humpback whale is up to 45 feet (14 m) long.

Long fins
The fins are knobbly and up to one-third of the total body length.

Baleen bristles

BARNACLES
These small animals, called barnacles, have settled on a gray whale's skin. There may be thousands of them on just one whale.

BALEEN PLATE
The special structures that these whales use to trap food are called baleen plates. They hang from the roof of a whale's mouth and work like sieves to capture small animals when the whale gulps in a mouthful of water. They are made of naillike protein, and bristles line the inside layers.

Sei whale

0	15 feet (5 m)	30 feet (10 m)	45 feet (15 m)	60 feet (20 m)

SEI WHALES
These large baleen whales are found in most of the world's oceans. They grow to nearly 65 feet (20 m) long and can weigh nearly 30 tons.

SPERM WHALE

Sperm whales are one of world's largest predators. They can dive deeper than any other mammal, swimming to the cold, dark depths of an ocean in search of prey, such as octopus or the enormous giant squid.

FACT FILE

DIET
Squid, octopuses, and fish

HABITAT
Open ocean, worldwide except very cold water

SPERM WHALE
PHYSETER MACROCEPHALUS

DEPTH
0 feet
(0 m)

9,750 feet
(3,000 m)

SIZE • UP TO 20.5 M

Large head
Sperm whales have the largest brains in the animal world.

Battle scars
Many sperm whales have scars from battles with giant squid.

⊕ LIGHT HEADED

A sperm whale has a waxy substance in its head called spermaceti. It may help the whale float, but the whale might also use spermaceti to make sounds.

A mother and calf sperm whale swimming close to the ocean surface.

WHALE DIVING

During its hunt for prey, a sperm whale can dive to 9,750 feet (3,000 m), and stay underwater for two hours.

A sperm whale diving head-first into the deep.

MOTHER AND CALF

A baby whale is called a calf. A sperm whale calf feeds on its mother's milk for 13 years! Sperm whales may attack boats if they think their young are in danger.

Huge, heavy body
A male sperm whale is three times heavier than a female. Each whale needs to eat about 1 ton of food a day!

SKULL

Sperm whales are toothed whales. They have up to 100 teeth on the lower jaw, but no teeth on the upper jaw.

Sharp teeth

TOOTHED WHALES

There are about 85 species of whale, and most of them are toothed whales. These mammals hunt for fish or other sea creatures and most of them are intelligent animals that live in family groups. Dolphins and porpoises are small toothed whales.

A lucky seal runs away from a charging killer whale as it beaches itself.

Stout body
A thick layer of blubber under a beluga's skin keeps it warm.

KILLER WHALE

Killer whales are also called orcas. They are deadly hunters that can swim onto the land to grab seals to eat.

NARWHAL

A narwhal's long "horn" is actually a tooth, or "tusk." No one knows exactly why narwhals grow such long tusks.

Long tusk

BELUGA WHALES

Beluga whales are small toot
whales that live in cold Arc
waters. They are sociab
and communicate v
clicking sounds. T
can even copy
noises made by
other animals.

Melon
The rounded
forehead of a
toothed whale is
called a melon.

Dolphin skull
Bottlenose dolphins
have a large beaklike
mouth with about 50
cone-shaped teeth.

DOLPHINS

Dolphins often gather in groups,
called pods. Atlantic spotted
dolphins hunt for fish and
crabs hiding on the sea floor.

*These spotted
dolphins will
live, hunt,
and breed
in a pod.*

Wide mouth
Beluga whales are popular with
divers, because they seem to smile!

WHITE WHALES

Male beluga whales can grow up to
18 feet (5.5 m) long and weigh 1.5 tons.
Its white body is perfect camouflage
against the ice and it has no dorsal fin
on its back.

WEDDELL SEAL

Weddell seals are plump seals with a thick layer of fat, or blubber, to keep them warm. They are able to survive in the icy Antarctic, which is the coldest place on Earth. Weddell seals hunt fish in the Southern Ocean, which surrounds Antarctica.

Tube body
A seal's body is the perfect shape for moving quickly through water.

Grey fur
Seals are mammals and they have a short, thick coat of hair to keep them warm.

FACT FILE

DIET
Fish, crustaceans, octopuses

HABITAT
Coastal waters around Antarctica

FEEDING TIME

An active adult Weddell seal will eat about 110 pounds (50 kg) of food in a day. If the water is dark or cloudy, they will track prey using their sensitive whiskers.

SUPERB SWIMMERS

These animals are superb swimmers and dive below thick layers of ice. They can stay underwater for 45 minutes at a time, foraging for food or trying to find new breathing holes.

A mother and pup pop their heads above the ice to breathe.

BREATHING HOLES

Weddell seals breathe air. They make holes in the ice so that they can surface and breathe between dives.

WEDDELL SEAL
LEPTONYCHOTES WEDDELLII

DEPTH

0 feet
(0 m)

2,400 feet
(740 m)

SIZE • 10 FEET (3 M)

The forward-facing eyes give a Weddell seal 3-D vision, which is vital for hunting.

UNDERWATER

Weddell seals are hunters. They use their big, forward-facing eyes to find fish, even in the dimly lit waters of a polar ocean.

Flippers
Seals have two pairs of flippers. The hind pair stops the seal from rolling in the water as it swims.

For the first few weeks, a baby seal is helpless and relies on its mother completely.

SEAL PUPS

Baby seals are called pups. Females give birth on the Antarctic ice, and the pups cannot swim until they are one to two weeks old.

SEALS AND SEA LIONS

Seals and sea lions are animals that live both on land and in the water. They belong to a group of swimming mammals called pinnipeds. Seals and sea lions are similar, but sea lions have ear flaps and longer, hairless front flippers which they use to "fly" through the water.

Flippers
By flapping their flippers, seals and sea lions can move through the water very quickly.

STELLER'S SEA LION
Steller's sea lions are large predators that chase squid, octopuses, fish, and even other seals in the Pacific Ocean.

CAPE FUR SEAL
Cape fur seals can twist and turn in the water, changing direction at speed when they are chasing fish.

Steller's sea lions are hunted by killer whales and white sharks.

Harp seal pups are covered in thick white fur.

HARP SEAL PUP
Harp seals are found in the Arctic. They can live to be 35 years old and they mostly hunt fish, such as cod.

An enormous male walrus resting on an ice floe.

WALRUS

Walruses are huge pinnipeds with enormous teeth, or tusks. They use their tusks to fight each other, break holes in the ice, and to pull themselves out of the water.

Ear
There is no ear flap on this seal's head.

Whiskers
These hairs help the seal to feel if fish are swimming nearby, even when it is too dark to see.

CLUMSY WALKERS

On land, the fins and flippers of seals and sea lions make them slow, clumsy walkers. However, unlike other marine mammals, such as whales and dolphins, seals and sea lions have to come on to dry land in order to give birth.

19

LEATHERBACK TURTLE

Leatherback turtles are the biggest of all the turtles that live in the sea. They breathe air, but they can dive deep in search of their favorite prey, jellyfish. They hold their breath for more than 30 minutes at a time.

A leatherback turtle will lay about 80 eggs in one go.

LAYING EGGS

Females use their flippers to dig a burrow in soft sand, and lay her eggs in it.

Once they have hatched, baby turtles have to race to the sea unprotected from waiting predators.

HATCHLINGS

When the hatchlings break out of their eggs they must find their way to the sea before any predator can catch them.

SPINES

The backward-pointing spines in a leatherback's mouth and throat stop slippery jellyfish from slipping back out of the turtle's mouth.

Soft shell
Most turtles have a hard shell, but the shell of this turtle is like leather.

LONG DISTANCE

Leatherbacks swim amazing distances between the places where they feed and the places where they lay their eggs. A one-way trip can be 3,750 miles (6,000 km)!

Flippers
Long, powerful flippers help a turtle to swim across enormous oceans, and deep beneath the water's surface.

FACT FILE

DIET
Jellyfish

HABITAT
Cool and warm open oceans

Ridges
The ridges on a leatherback's shell help it to move smoothly through the water.

LEATHERBACK
DERMOCHELYS CORIACEA

DEPTH

0 feet
(0 m)

3,900 feet
(1,200 m)

SIZE • 7 FEET (2 M)

LARGE SIZE

Leatherbacks are the largest of all turtles. While they can grow to a total length of more than 7 feet (2 m), their flippers can stretch to more than 8 feet (2.5 m) across.

0   2 feet   4 feet   6 feet
       (0.6 m)   (1.2 m)   (1.8 m)

21

OCEAN REPTILES

Most reptiles live on land, but some types have taken to a life at sea. Like all reptiles, they lay their eggs on land, although some sea snakes give birth to their young in water. Marine reptiles are more common in warm oceans than cool ones.

BANDED SEA KRAIT
The bright stripes of banded sea kraits act as a warning and show that they are venomous sea snakes. They return to the land to mate and lay eggs.

Banded sea krait

BEAKED SEA SNAKE
Beaked sea snakes are one of the deadliest of all snakes, with powerful venom that can kill a human quickly.

Feet
The clawed feet are webbed, so a crocodile can swim quickly through the water.

Snout
Crocodiles can open their mouths underwater because a special flap at the back of their throat closes to stop water rushing in.

Nostrils
A crocodile's nostrils are at the tip of its long snout. It can breathe out underwater, but must return to the surface to breathe in.

SALTWATER CROCODILE

Crocodiles can grow huge, but saltwater crocodiles—or "salties"—are the monsters of the family. They may grow to 23 feet (7 m) long, and can live in rivers or the sea.

GREEN TURTLE

Green turtles feed on plants that grow in the sea. Like most sea turtles they are at risk of becoming extinct.

The olive sea snake can close its nostrils when underwater.

OLIVE SEA SNAKE

An olive sea snake's nostrils are on the top of its head, so it can breathe at the sea's surface. Unlike land snakes, it also has a flattened rear section to its tail, which is ideal for swimming.

Green turtle

GREAT WHITE SHARK

Fin

The large fin on the back, called the dorsal fin, is the shape of a triangle.

A lean, mean powerful hunter with razor-sharp teeth—this is one of the world's most impressive predators. Few animals inspire as much fear as a great white shark, but these big beasts rarely eat humans.

A great white breaches with a helpless seal in its mouth.

BREACHING

Great whites can leap out of the water to catch their prey. This is called breaching.

SENSITIVE HUNTER

Great white sharks are ambush hunters. They can sense prey from far away. They can then accelerate to speeds of more than 35 mph (55 km/h) to catch an animal—before crunching down on it with their massive jaws.

FACT FILE

DIET
Large animals such as seals, tuna, sharks, sea birds, and turtles

HABITAT
The open ocean and coasts, especially shallow water

0   7 feet (2 m)   14 feet (4 m)   21 feet (6 m)

GREAT WHITE SHARK
CARCHARODON CARCHARIAS

DEPTH

0 feet
(0 m)

6,175 feet
(1,900 m)

SIZE • 19 FEET (6 M)

Gill slits
There are five large gill slits on each side of the head.

Powerful tail
Packed with muscles, the shark moves this from side to side to push itself through the water.

TEETH
A great white has about 30 teeth in a row on each jaw, but there are another four rows of teeth behind those. As one falls out, another moves forward to take its place.

Serrated teeth
The edges of the teeth are serrated (jagged) so that they can slice through prey easily.

Hunting fish
Great white sharks are the largest predatory fish on the planet. They can weigh more than 2 tons.

Great whites are one of the few sharks that spy hop.

SHARKS

Sharks are fish that hunt other animals to eat. They have rough skin and soft skeletons, like skates and rays. There are about 400 different types of shark, from small ones that live near the seabed to large hunters of the open ocean.

WHALE SHARK

Whale sharks are not just the largest sharks, they are the largest fish in the world. They may be big, but whale sharks are harmless to humans and only eat small animals, such as plankton.

HAMMERHEAD SHARK

Hammerhead sharks have strangely shaped heads. This head shape may help a hammerhead to find its prey, and change direction quickly.

Spotted skin
Every whale shark has a different pattern on its back.

Wide mouth
The mouth measures about 7 feet (2 m) across, but the teeth are tiny.

A sand tiger shark usually swims with its mouth open, showing the rows of jagged teeth.

SHARK SKIN

Sharks do not have scales. Their skin is covered in tiny "teeth" instead. They contain a hard substance called enamel, just like our teeth.

SAND TIGERS

Sand tiger sharks are often called "raggedtooths." Their long, pointy teeth are perfect for gripping hold of slippery fish and squid.

Huge body
Most whale sharks can grow up to 36 feet (11 m) long.

⊕ SEA GIANT

A whale shark can weigh in at more than 20 tons —that's the weight of four elephants. It is one of only three species of filter-feeding shark, the other two being the basking shark and the very rare megamouth.

Friendly fish
Smaller fish often swim near whale sharks, hiding from animals that might want to eat them!

MIGRATIONS

Many animals go on long journeys to find food or a mate. These journeys are called migrations, and some of the world's greatest migrations happen in the oceans.

Ball of fish
Thousands of sardines gather together to make a baitball to try and stay safe from predators.

BLUE WHALE

Blue whales spend the summer in the cold waters of the Arctic or Antarctic, where they feed. They then swim thousands of miles to breed in warm waters during the winter.

BLUE SHARK

Female blue sharks go on an incredible migration of about 10,000 miles (16,000 km) to breed. These sharks give birth to live young.

Large eyes

Large pectoral fins

BALL OF SARDINES

Billions of sardines gather in huge shoals near South Africa in the winter. They are here to feast on tiny plankton. Hungry predators follow the sardines on their migration.

Five pairs of swimming legs

ANTARCTIC KRILL

These tiny animals go on long vertical journeys in the ocean. This means they travel up or down, in the water in search of food.

SOCKEYE SALMON

Sockeye salmon live in the ocean until it is time to spawn (lay eggs). They leave the oceans and swim to lakes or rivers to mate.

The baitball distracts predators

Predators
Large predators, such as seals, sharks, and sailfish, come to feast on a baitball.

29

RATFISH

Ratfish are peculiar fish that are close relatives of sharks, skates, and rays. They have stout, flabby bodies, rough skin, and no scales. Ratfish normally swim close to the seabed where they find crunchy animals to eat, crushing them with their platelike teeth.

FACT FILE

DIET
Crustaceans, echinoderms, worms, fish

HABITAT
Near the seafloor in the Northeast Pacific Ocean

Long, slender tail
This animal is called a ratfish because of the shape and size of its tail.

Long fins
Fins run along the length of the whiplike tail.

SPECIAL CLASPERS

Like male sharks, male ratfish have special claspers on their bodies (visible just behind the lower fins). They use them to clasp (hold) onto females at mating time.

Ratfish lay their eggs in sand or mud on the seabed

RATFISH EGG

Female ratfish lay a single spoon-shaped egg every 10-14 days at breeding time. Each egg is protected inside a rubbery egg case.

RATFISH
HYDROLAGUS COLLIEI

DEPTH

0 feet
(0 m)

9,750 feet
(3,000 m)

SIZE • 1 FOOT (30 CM)

Despite its large eyes, most of its prey is found using the fish's sense of smell.

RABBIT FACE
Ratfish have large eyes, broad mouths, and strange heads that are often said to look like rabbit heads.

Spotted skin
Spots on the skin help a fish to blend into the sea floor so predators cannot see it.

⊕ VENOMOUS FISH
A ratfish has a long spine on its back, just in front of the dorsal fin. This spine is connected to a venom gland. Although the venom is not fatal to humans, it can produce a painful burning sensation that lasts for a couple of days.

RAYS AND CARTILAGE FISH

Most fish have bony skeletons, but there is another large group of fish in the oceans—the cartilaginous fish. These fish have skeletons made of a rubbery material called cartilage, instead of bone. This is the same material that is found in your nose and outer ears. Cartilaginous fish include sharks, ratfish, rays, and skates.

Tail
Manta ray tails are usually shorter than their bodies.

Electric ray

ELECTRIC RAY
There are 14 species, or type, of electric ray. They catch their prey by stunning them with a powerful jolt of electricity.

STINGRAY
Stingrays usually swim near the seabed. They defend themselves using a whiplike tail that has a venomous spine.

Stingray tail

A stingray flips up its tail and spine when it is threatened.

Fins
A manta ray's huge fins beat like wings, so the fish appears to slowly fly through the water.

Guitarfish take their name from the rounded guitar shape of their heads.

GUITARFISH
Guitarfish live in warm coastal waters, where they prowl above the sea floor looking for crustaceans and prawns to eat.

 ## MANTA RAY
Manta rays are enormous, peaceful fish that feed on plankton and can measure more than 23 feet (7 m) across. They may be big, but they are graceful fish that can even leap out of the water. Manta rays give birth to their young.

Mouth horns
The large mouth opens to suck in water and tiny living things called plankton. Horn-shaped edges force plankton into the fish's mouth.

EAGLE RAY
Eagle rays are kite-shaped fish that often live in large shoals. They are good swimmers, and have a venomous spine on their tail.

SAILFISH

Sailfish are the fastest swimming fish in the sea. They have huge saillike fins that help them to reach top speeds of about 45 mph (70 km/h), and to leap out of the water. Sailfish often hunt in a group and usually swim near the ocean surface.

Microscopic juvenile

JUVENILES
Female sailfish produce about 4 million eggs at a time! The young do not grow their bills until they are about 0.2 inches (5 mm) long.

Large body
A sailfish's body is streamlined, which means it is the right shape for moving quickly through water.

Huge dorsal fin
The fin on a sailfish's back is tall and almost stretches the whole length of the body.

SAILFISH
ISTIOPHORUS PLATYPTERUS

DEPTH

0 feet
(0 m)

650 feet
(200 m)

SIZE • 10 FEET (3 M)

SUPER SPEED
Sailfish need speed to catch the fast-swimming fish, such as mackerel and sardines, that they prefer. These long-nosed swimmers belong to a family of fish called billfishes.

FACT FILE

DIET
Schooling fish, octopuses, and squid

HABITAT
Warm, open oceans

POINTED NOSE

A sailfish's mouth is long and slender. It is called a bill because it looks like the slim bill of a bird.

The bill can measure nearly one-third of the fish's length.

Bill
The fish's upper jaw is about twice as long as its lower jaw.

⊕ ALL CHANGE

Sailfish have the ability to change the color of their skin. When they become excited, they can create a range of colors, including grays, purples, and silvers to confuse prey.

Sailfish sometimes use their large sails to herd prey together.

HUNTING FISH

The fish uses its swordlike bill to slash at shoaling fish. It then swallows any fish that have been injured or stunned.

OTHER BONY FISH

There are about 31,000 species of bony fish and most of them live in the oceans, ranging from tiny dwarf goby to the giant ocean sunfish. Although they have skeletons of bone, these fish come in all shapes and sizes. Some of them hunt other animals to eat, while others eat plants.

 ## SUNFISH

Sunfish are the largest bony fish in the world. They live in warm waters and swim slowly, nibbling at jellyfish. If a sunfish is scared it might jump out of the water.

PORCUPINE FISH

When a porcupine fish is resting it may look odd, but it does not look too scary. When it fills itself with air, the fish's body turns into a ball of spines that a predator won't try and swallow!

LIONFISH

Lionfish live around coral reefs. Their bold stripes warn other animals that their fins are covered in venomous spines.

Ocean sunfish larva

Disklike body
The body is rounded but very slender, and it looks like a disk, or a sun.

Tails and fins
Sunfish have unusual tails with a frilled edge. The fins are shaped like triangles and slice through the water like blades.

TINY LARVAE

Sunfish larvae are only 0.1 inch (2.5 mm) long and will grow many millions of times in size before reaching maturity. Some larvae are also covered in spines, which they lose as they grow.

LEAFY SEADRAGON

Leafy seadragons are a type of seahorse. Their incredible body shape helps them to hide in seaweed.

Fins look like seaweed

Hagfish can tie themselves in knots to escape from predators.

HAGFISH

Hagfish have long eellike bodies that are covered in sticky slime. They do not have jaws, and some scientists think they are not really fish at all!

DEEP-SEA ANGLERFISH

This terrifying-looking fish has a long thin fin just above its mouth, topped with a light. This fin and light is used like a fishing rod to attract prey, including small fish and squid, which probably mistake the light for a tasty snack.

Small fin
As they don't have to move quickly to catch prey, most anglerfish are slow swimmers.

Stretchy body
An anglerfish can stretch its body to engulf prey twice its size.

DEEP-SEA ANGLERFISH
MELANOCETUS JOHNSONI

DEPTH

650 feet
(200 m)

6,500 feet
(2,000 m)

SIZE • 8 INCHES (20 CM)

ACTUAL SIZE

0   1 inch
(2.5 cm)

LITTLE AND LARGE
Female anglerfish are about 20 cm long, while the male (left) can be less than a tenth of this size. Females are the only ones to have lights.

HIDING IN THE DARK

Living at depths of between 650–6,500 feet (200–2,000 m), deep-sea anglerfish are colored dark brown or black. This camouflages them in the black water.

Skeleton
The red areas are the fish's bones.

OPEN WIDE

Its thin, flexible bones, jellylike skin and stretchy stomach allow the anglerfish to open its mouth wide enough to swallow prey much larger than itself.

Sharp teeth
Its needlelike teeth pierce the flesh of its victims.

MALES AND FEMALES

In some species of anglerfish, the much-smaller males attach themselves to the females, feeding off nutrients in the females' blood.

ANGLERFISH

Lure
This contains millions of light-making bacteria.

There are more than 200 species of anglerfish. They come in many shapes and sizes, including the round football fish and the long, thin wonder fish. In some species, the teeth can be pushed back so that they don't stop anything entering the mouth.

Humpback anglerfish
Females of this anglerfish species can grow up to 8 inches (20 cm) long, and they are found at depths of up to 6,500 feet (2,000 m).

LITTLE GUY

During mating, the tiny male of most anglerfish species attaches himself to the female. His body then fuses with hers.

Sharp teeth
Backward-facing teeth stop prey from escaping.

OUTER SHELL
Some anglerfish young are covered in a thick protective membrane when they are born.

Short tail

WONDER FISH
Unlike other angler fish, the 3.5-inch (9-cm) long wonder fish's lure is inside its mouth.

⊕ ALL DEPTHS
Anglerfish range in size from 1.5–35 inches (4–90 cm) in length. Some live in shallow waters, but the deepest living are found more than 1.25 miles (2 km) down. Many are slow swimmers. Some even lie on the ocean bed, mouth open, waiting for prey to come into range.

Like a ball
The fish has a short, sphere-shaped body.

⊕ SUDDEN BURSTS
While anglerfish spend most of their time hovering in the water or moving slowly, some have been seen making short bursts of speed to avoid hunters.

FOOTBALL FISH
The first species of angler fish ever discovered, the football fish ranges in size from 1.5–15 inches (4–40 cm) and is found at depths of up to 3,250 feet (1,000 m).

HATCHETFISH

Hatchetfish are creatures of the twilight zone, where there is little light. However, they also swim up toward the lighter zones to feed during the night. About 50 species of hatchetfish have been discovered so far.

Flat, shiny body
This helps to reflect any small amount of light.

FACT FILE

DIET
Fish, plankton, and small crustaceans

HABITAT
Deep water in warm areas of the oceans

Tube-shaped eyes
They point upwards, toward the light.

ACTUAL • SIZE

HATCHETFISH
STERNOPTYCHINAE

DEPTH

0 feet
(0 m)

3,250 feet
(1,000 m)

SIZE • 3 INCHES (7.5 CM)

BIG EYES

A hatchetfish's strange eyes are fixed looking upwards and are shaped to catch as much light as possible. The fish uses them to look for any prey swimming above.

0	1 inch (2.5 cm)	2 inches (5 cm)	3 inches (7.5 cm)	

LIGHT ORGANS

A hatchetfish has special light-making organs called photophores. These glow to match any light coming from the surface above, hiding the fish from any predators looking up from the depths below.

BELLY LIGH

A hatchetfish's
are found lining ft
pointing down into the u
inky blackness.

Axe body
The fish's body is the shape of an ax (or "hatchet").

Photophores
Light-making organs line the fish's body.

MARINE HATCHETFISH

There are about 40 species of marine hatchetfish. There is another group of freshwater hatchetfish, but they are not related to these sea-living species.

FLASHLIGHT FISH

It may be dark in the deep ocean, but there are fish that can make light to help them find other animals to eat. Flashlight fish usually stay in the darkest parts of the ocean, but will travel to shallow water to feed on small crustaceans at night.

FACT FILE

DIET
Small animals, especially crustaceans

HABITAT
Deep waters in warmer parts of the ocean

Slender body
The body is covered with shiny scales.

Large eyes
Eyes that are big can gather more light than ones that are small.

Photophore
This is the place where light is made. Fish can have photophores on different parts of their bodies.

GLOW IN THE DARK

Like anglerfish, flashlight fish use their lights to lure prey. They also use their lights to communicate, and to confuse animals that want to eat them.

FLASHLIGHT FISH
ANOMALOPIDAE

DEPTH

0 feet
(0 m)

13,000 feet
(4,000 m)

SIZE • 3 INCHES (7.5 CM)

ACTUAL • SIZE

| 0 | 1 inch (2.5 cm) | 2 inches (5 cm) | 3 inches (7.5 cm) |

BIOLUMINESCENT LIGHT ORGAN

Fish make light in their light organs when two chemicals are mixed together, or the light is made by bacteria that live on the fish's body. Flashlight fish control how much light is on show by covering the light organs with a special flap.

The one-fin flashlight fish is found in the Indian and Pacific oceans.

Photophore covered by flap

Photophore

NIGHT FISH

SNIPE EEL

A snipe eel may look like a long piece of string, but it is a deep-sea fish with a peculiar mouth, big eyes, and a very long backbone. It has large eyes to see in the dark ocean waters and its jaws are lined with tiny teeth for catching food.

Long body
Snipe eels have up to 750 bones (vertebrae) in their backbones. That is more than any other animal.

Snipe eel larva

The young have transparent, leaf-shaped bodies.

SNIPE EEL YOUNG

After hatching, a young snipe eel will float near the sea's surface for several months, before sinking to the seabed and changing into an adult.

 ## NIGHT-TIME FEEDERS

Snipe eels probably swim toward the surface of the sea at night, to feed on shrimps and shrimplike animals. They hang in the water with their mouths open, trapping their prey with backward-pointing teeth. Once snagged, the prey is then worked into the mouth and swallowed.

FACT FILE

DIET
Shrimp and other crustaceans

HABITAT
Cool and warm oceans

DUCK HEAD

The snipe eel is sometimes called a deep sea duck, because the beaklike mouth makes it look like a duck!

The tips of the snipe eel's long, slender jaws curve apart.

Deep fish
Bobtail snipe eels have been found at depths of 16,250 feet (5,000 m).

Bobtail snipe eel

BOBTAIL SNIPE EEL

Bobtail snipe eels live in very deep water and they are almost blind. They grow to about 6 inches (15 cm) long. Although they share the same name with snipe eels, they belong to a different family.

Long lightweights
Snipe eels may have a body that is 7 feet (2 m) long, but they will only weigh 1.1 pounds (500 g) at most.

SNIPE EEL
NEMICHTHYIDAE

DEPTH

300 feet (90 m)

5,850 feet (1,800 m)

SIZE • 7 FEET (2 M)

EELS

Eels are long, slender fish. There are about 740 different types of eel and they all have many backbones—vertebrae—in their long, bendy bodies. Most eels have a smooth or slimy skin, without any scales and they feed on other animals.

Conger eels will eat a range of prey, including crabs, fish, and worms.

CONGER EEL

Conger eels can grow huge and powerful. They have been known to attack divers, and can deliver a nasty bite. They are the longest type of eel and can grow to 10 feet (3 m) in length.

The stripes make the banded snake eel look like a venomous sea snake.

BANDED SNAKE EEL

Banded snake eels hunt at night, and find their prey using their good sense of smell. They feed on fish and crustaceans.

Slimy skin
Moray eels can make a toxic slime that coats their skin.

Bold patterns
This moray is called a leopard moray because of the patterns on its skin.

Ribbon eels grow up to 3.5 feet (1 m) long and can live for 20 years.

RIBBON EEL

Ribbon eels are small moray eels. They hide under rocks or in sand, and come out to catch small fish or shrimps that swim by.

MORAY EEL

Moray eels often hide in a shallow sea's shadows. They wait for fish, or other animals to swim by, then pounce on them. Some moray eels can be more than 10 feet (3 metres) long.

GARDEN EELS

Garden eels hide in burrows in the seabed and poke their heads out to feed. They tend to live in groups and look like plants growing in a garden.

Strong jaws
The mouth is lined with large sharp teeth

LIVING IN GROUPS

There is safety in numbers in the deep ocean. Animals that live on land have plenty of places to keep out of sight, but in the huge expanse of the ocean there are few places to hide. Instead, animals often stay together in big groups.

Shoal
A large group of fish is called a school, or a shoal.

FISH SCALES
Fish scales overlap, like roof tiles, so water can flow over them easily. They are also flat, which helps to reflect light.

*A **shoal** of hammerhead sharks swimming near the Galápagos Islands.*

HAMMERHEAD SHARKS
Most sharks live alone, but hammerheads are unusual because they often live together. They split up when it is time to eat, and hunt alone.

Big-eye trevallies
These fish can grow to more than 4 feet (1.2 m) long.

Silvery scales
Scales can work like mirrors, to reflect light.

About 8,000 species of fish live on coral reefs around the world.

⊕ BIGEYE TREVALLIES

When a big, swirling ball of fish is on the move the light dances off their silvery scales, and makes them look like one large animal. These reflections also confuse any predators.

CORAL REEF SHOAL

Groups of fish are common around a coral reef. There is enough food for them all to eat, and finding a mate is easier when you live together. There are plenty of eyes looking out for predators and plenty of places to hide.

Barracuda can swim at speeds of more than 25 mph (40 km/h) to catch prey.

SHOAL OF BARRACUDA

Barracudas have long, sleek bodies and can grow to 7 feet (2 m) long. Adults usually swim alone, but young ones gather in large shoals.

DRAGONFISH

With bristling teeth, flashing lights, and a feeler dangling from its chin, the dragonfish is a monster of the deep. The females are larger than males and live for several breeding seasons. Males live only a few weeks.

Lighting up
Dragonfish make their own light through chemical reactions inside their bodies.

BLACK DRAGONFISH
IDIACANTHUS FASCIOLA

DEPTH

1,625 feet
(500 m)

5,850 feet
(1,800 m)

SIZE • 15 INCHES (40 CM)
(female)

Big teeth
Sloane's viperfish has the largest teeth of any fish, relative to the size of its head.

IN THE FAMILY

Other monstrous relations of the black dragonfish also have light organs and sharp teeth. They include loosejaws and viperfish.

The barbel is tipped with a luminescent organ.

COLORS

Unlike most other bioluminescent fish, the dragonfish can produce different colors from its photophores.

Light organ
A female has a light organ behind each eye and rows of small lights along her sides.

FEARSOME FEMALES

The female dragonfish has a long, black, streamlined body and a huge mouth with sharp teeth. Males are smaller, pale brown, and have no teeth or barbels.

Sharp teeth
Females' teeth are long, barbed fangs.

Barbel
A female also has a long feeler called a barbel.

Small head
Compared to its body, the female's head is small and dominated by its wide jaw.

Dragonfish larva

GROWING UP

Dragonfish young hatch from eggs. Before becoming adults, they grow into transparent larvae whose eyes stick out from the sides of their bodies on long stalks.

FACT FILE

DIET
Females eat small fish, but males do not feed once they are fully grown

HABITAT
Depths of the ocean, surface when feeding

DEEP-SEA FISH

Far below the sunlit surface lies a zone of darkness inhabited by some strange fish. This area has some light, as many fish create their own through bioluminescence. Most food drifts down to the depths from the surface, but some creatures do hunt.

Long, thin fish
Gulper eels will grow to about 3.5 feet (1 m) in length.

Unusual fish
The body has no scales, pelvic fins, or swim bladder.

Giant mouth
Lined with teeth. the mouth acts like a net, opening and ambushing prey much larger that itself.

Big mouth
The gulper eel is also called the pelican eel because its mouth looks like that of the big-throated bird.

GULPER EEL

A gulper eel's long, thin body is not ideal for swimming fast. Instead, it uses the luminescent organ on its tail to attract prey. Gulper eels have been found living at depths of up to 9,750 feet (3,000 m).

Barrier
The teeth prevent prey from escaping before they are swallowed.

LIGHT ORGANS

Unlike anglerfish, the light organ of the gulper eel is found at the end of the tail. In order to lure prey near its mouth, the eel has to pull the tip of its tail round toward its head.

SABERTOOTH FISH

This small fierce-looking predator has tubular eyes that point upward and large pointed front teeth, which give it its name.

Huge stomach
This fish's stomach has stretched to fit in a fish.

BLACK SWALLOWER

This fish can also swallow prey much larger than itself. It inhabits depths of 8,900 feet (2,745 m) and feeds on bony fish, which are swallowed whole into its enormous, stretchy stomach.

OARFISH

Oarfish are the longest bony fish in the world, growing up to 35 feet (11 m) long. Although they sometimes hunt at depths of 3,250 feet (1,000 m), oarfish sometimes swim near the surface, and may get washed ashore.

Terrifying tail
The whiplike tail glows pink at the end and also helps the eel to move.

Sea monster
These strange fish may be to blame for stories of giant sea serpents!

MICROLIFE

The oceans are home to billions of tiny animals and plants. They are too small for us to see and we can only look at them with the help of a microscope. They are called microlife, or plankton, and other animals depend on them for food.

MICROLIFE

DEPTH

0 feet
(0 m)

325 feet
(100 m)

**SIZE • UP TO 0.5 INCH
(1 CM)**

Tail
Tiny animals use threadlike tails to swim.

PHYTOPLANKTON BLOOM

When conditions are just right, tiny plant plankton can grow into huge swarms, called a bloom. Some blooms, like this one in the Bay of Biscay, can be seen from space.

0	60	120	180 miles
0	100	200	300 km

Copepod
These animals have two long antennae. They are members of the crustacean family.

This microscope image of plant plankton has been enlarged 20 times.

Plant plankton

PLANT PLANKTON

Plant plankton, or phytoplankton, is made up of tiny plants that use the sun's energy to make food. They make the oxygen we breathe.

⊕ ANIMALS

Animal plankton is known as zooplankton. The name comes from the Greek meaning "animal wanderer."

Float along
Some plankton can swim, but they mostly float in the ocean.

Ocean young
Some tiny animals are the eggs and young of fish, jellyfish, and other sea creatures.

⊕ MICRO ZOO

Animals and plants that are too small for us to see are described as microscopic. Larger plankton feed on smaller plankton, and they are eaten by fish, which are eaten by even bigger fish, and so on. Without these tiny living things, nothing else would live in the oceans.

FACT FILE

DIET
Tiny plants

HABITAT
All the world's oceans, near the surface

57

TINY CREATURES

Small animals and plants are the food for bigger animals in the sea. While some of these creatures have simple bodies and lives, others are the young of bigger animals, such as octopuses, that have just hatched. Young sea animals are often called larvae.

WATER FLEA

Water fleas are transparent, so it s possible to see their body parts nside. They use their antennae to swim around.

Soft skin
The octopus's soft skin is colored and patterned.

Tiny version
An octopus larva looks like the adult, but it is much smaller.

More than 600 species of water flea have been named so far.

 PACIFIC GIANT OCTOPUS LARVA

A giant Pacific octopus is one of the biggest animals in the ocean, but its larvae (young) measure about 0.4 inches (1 cm) when they hatch from their eggs.

STARFISH LARVA

A female starfish lays millions of eggs. Each larva grows "arms" out from its body and it takes two months to become an adult.

HEART URCHIN LARVA

A sea urchin larva floats in the water for several weeks before it settles on the seabed and grows into an adult. It has several arms that stretch out around the mouth.

Arm with tiny suckers

This tiny octopus larva has only just hatched.

HUGE NUMBERS

Octopus eggs are produced in huge numbers—about 45,000 each time. The larvae hatch and grow quickly, although very few of them will survive to maturity.

JAPANESE SPIDER CRAB

Japanese spider crabs are the largest crabs in the world and they can measure 13 feet (4 m) from toe to toe—about as wide as a car. These giant crustaceans stay on the seabed, searching for food to eat.

Long legs
The crab's body does not get much bigger as it ages, but its legs get longer.

SPIDER CRAB
MACROCHEIRA KAEMPFERI

DEPTH

160 feet
(50 m)

1,950 feet
(600 m)

SIZE • 13 FEET (4 M)

FACT FILE

DIET
Small animals, dead animals, seaweed

HABITAT
The sandy or rocky seabed of coastal areas

SMALL MOUTHS

Japanese spider crabs tear up food into small pieces with their pincers before putting it in their mouths.

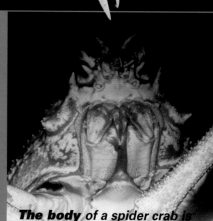

The body of a spider crab is about 15 inches (40 cm) across.

Spines
*Spines grow
between the eyes.*

Scavengers
Japanese spider crabs
feed off the remains
of dead sea creatures
and anything else
they can find.

Carapace
*A crab's tough shell is
called a carapace. It is
red, tan, or orange with
blotches of white.*

**Indonesian
spider crab**

*Indonesian spider crabs sometimes
cover their bodies with stinging hydrozoa.*

CAMOUFLAGE
Some types of spider crab, such as
the Indonesian spider crab, are
called "decorators" because they
cover their bodies with bits of
seaweed or small animals.

⊕ WEAK LEGS
The legs of a
Japanese sea crab
are spindly. The
weight of its body is
supported by water
so the legs do not
need to be strong.
However, this also
means that they are
easily snapped.
Luckily, the crabs can
grow new legs to
replace ones that
they lose!

OCEAN ARTHROPODS

It is thought that about three-quarters of all types of animals are arthropods, including insects. Arthropods have a tough outer skin, a body that is divided into segments, and jointed legs. Crabs, prawns, lobsters, and sea spiders are all types of arthropod.

HORSESHOE CRAB

Horseshoe crabs are living fossils. They are the last members of a family of arthropods that lived 300 million years ago. They are more closely related to spiders than to crabs. They walk about the ocean floor looking for worms and molluscs to eat.

Green, paddle-shaped antenna

The peacock mantis has the fastest punch of any living animal.

SEA SPIDER

Despite their name, sea spiders are not really spiders! They have between 8 and 12 legs, and feed on corals and sponges.

PEACOCK MANTIS

Peacock mantises are among the most colorful of all sea creatures. They are shrimps with incredible eyesight, and a powerful punch.

Long, stiff tail

SPINY LOBSTER

Spiny lobsters hide in their underwater dens in the day to stay safe. At night, they come out to hunt for sea snails, urchins, clams, and crabs.

Spiny lobsters have long, thin spiny antennae.

Tough shell
The shell, or carapace, is the shape of a horseshoe.

Four pairs of legs

Hidden from view
Underneath, there are five pairs of gills an four pairs of walking legs.

Mouth
The crab's mou lies in the mid of its legs.

Top side
The top shell or carapace completely covers the body.

FIREFLY SQUID

Light organs
Two of the arms contain light-emitting organs.

Arms
Like all squid, the firefly squid has eight arms.

In spring, millions of tiny firefly squid come to the surface to breed. They produce glittering lights to frighten or confuse predators and also to attract a mate. However, in Japan firefly squid are a delicacy and the lights attract fishermen as well.

JAPANESE FIREFLY SQUID
WATASENIA SCINTILLANS

DEPTH

650 feet
(200 m)

1,300 feet
(400 m)

SIZE • 3 INCHES (7.5 CM)

FIREFLY SQUID

The firefly squid's body and tentacles contain small light organs, which produce blue-white lights. The squid can alter the color, intensity, and angle of its lights.

SMALL BUT SPEEDY
Japanese firefly squid are only the length of the human finger but they can swim up to 25 mph (40 km/h).

·ACTUAL· ·SIZE·

0	1 inch (2.5 cm)	2 inches (5 cm)	3 inches (7.5 cm)

DEADLY LURE

As well being used to attract a mate, the firefly squid uses its light display to lure prey. Once it is close enough, the squid will grab the prey with its arms and pull it towards the squid's mouth.

FACT FILE

DIET
Shrimp, crabs, fish, and plankton

HABITAT
Depths of the ocean, surface when feeding

Impressive eyes
A firefly squid has three types of light-sensitive cells in its retina.

Glowing lights
The body is covered with rows of glowing lights.

DEEP-SEA SQUID

The deep-sea squid produces so much light that it would show up on a photograph taken in the dark, without a flash.

Tentacles
The largest light-producing organs are found in the tentacles.

OCEAN MOLLUSCS

There are more than 50,000 types, or species, of mollusc in the world and most of them live in the oceans. Many molluscs have shells and live near the seabed, but octopuses and squid are smart, soft-bodied swimmers of the open sea.

Shell
The nautilus's soft body is protected by a hard shell.

Eye
Even though it has a large eye, a nautilus has poor vision and relies more on smell.

NUDIBRANCH
Nudibranchs, or sea slugs, are some of the most colorful of all ocean creatures. Their colors and patterns warn predators that their flesh tastes bad or is poisonous.

CONE SHELL
Many molluscs are protected by shells, but cone shells have an extra way to stay safe—they are one of the most venomous animals on the planet. Inside the shell, the animal has a spear-like barb that is fired at a fish and injects deadly venom.

Some cone shells produce a venom that is deadly to humans.

Head
There are up to 90 tentacles surrounding the head.

NAUTILUS

These molluscs live in the warm waters around Asia and Australia. They use their tentacles to catch prey, such as shrimps. They move around by sucking in water and then forcing it out to create a high-pressure jet to push them along.

Changing skin
The skin color can change all the time, even when the cuttlefish is resting.

CUTTLEFISH

Cuttlefish can change the color of their skin in an instant. They often live on coral reefs.

GIANT OCTOPUS

A giant octopus can grow to about 10 feet (3 m) long, and can live in deep water up to 2,450 feet (750 m). These predators crawl on the seafloor, or swim.

Head

LIVING FOSSILS

Nautilus are often called living fossils, because they are the last example of a group of animals called nautiloids, which scientists believe evolved nearly 500 million years ago.

COMB JELLY

FACT FILE

DIET
Plankton and young fish

HABITAT
Open ocean and coasts, especially warm waters

Comb jellies are soft-bodied animals that swim gracefully through the sea. They prey on other animals, especially young fish, which they catch using sticky tentacles that they trail through the water. As they move, they shimmer with beautiful colors.

Glowing lights
Comb jellies have rows of light-producing cells along their bodies, which they flash to startle predators.

SEE-THROUGH GUTS

This comb jelly has swallowed a krill—a shrimplike animal—which can be seen inside the jelly's gut.

SHAPES AND SIZES

There are about 200 different types of comb jelly. They come in various shapes and sizes and many have long trailing arms, which they use to catch prey.

GLOWING LIGHTS

The beautiful colors of a comb jelly can be seen as it moves. Some comb jellies produce lights by mixing chemicals, while others glow because they have eaten other bioluminescent creatures.

⊕ SWIMMING HAIRS

The body of a comb jelly is covered in rows of tiny moving "hairs." When the hairs beat together, the comb jelly moves forward. As the hairs beat, they release glowing particles, creating a luminous cloud behind the comb jelly.

COMB JELLY
CTENOPHORA

DEPTH

0 feet
(0 m)

22,750 feet
(7,000 m)

SIZE • UP TO 5 FEET (1.5 M)

Soft bodies
The body is soft, with no bones or shells to protect it.

0

4 inches
(10 cm)

8 inches
(20 cm)

12 inches
(30 cm)

OCEAN INVERTEBRATES

Animals that do not have backbones are called invertebrates. Many of the ocean's animals are invertebrates. Although they do not have a skeleton to support their organs and limbs, they can grow big because the water supports their weight.

BLUE SEA SQUIRT

Sea squirts look like blobs of jelly on the seabed, but they are busy little animals that suck in seawater, and eat any animals that come with it.

CORAL

A blue starfish rests on a coral. The coral is rocky, but it has been built by small invertebrates. Tiny polyps live inside the coral and build it.

Stinging tentacles

SEA ANEMONE

Sea anemones rest on the seabed. Their stinging tentacles capture animals that float or swim past.

JELLYFISH

A black sea nettle is a type of giant jellyfish. These invertebrates can grow huge, and their tentacles can reach 23 feet (7 m) long or more.

Bell
This is the jellyfish's body. It can grow to 3.5 feet (1 m) in width.

Long tentacles
They are covered with stinging cells that stun or kill their prey.

SPONGE

Red sea sponges look like plants, but they are animals that suck water into their bodies to feed on the little animals in the water. Sea sponges are stuck to the seabed.

Powerful sting
A sea nettle's sting will kill small sea creatures, but is not lethal to humans.

STINGING CELLS

The thousands of stinging cells that cover the sea nettle's tentacles are called nematocysts. These release a venom-covered dart when touched.

STARFISH

Starfish have tough bodies that are usually covered in spines, and they use their arms to creep along the seabed. They eat other animals by pushing their stomachs out of their mouths to start digesting their food straight away!

Spiny arms
Most starfish have five arms, but some have more.

The larval stage of a starfish.

LARVA STAGE

Starfish release many eggs into the sea. They hatch into larvae that float in the plankton. Eventually, they settle and grow into adults.

Tough shell
The shell of a starfish is made of lots of small pieces, or "plates."

CROWN OF THORNS STARFISH

Crown of thorns starfish devour coral polyps in a coral reef, causing terrible damage to these precious places.

A crown of thorns starfish crawls over a coral reef.

⊕ ECHINODERMS

Brittle stars and starfish belong to an animal group called the echinoderms. They do not have heads. Brittlestars raise their arms into the water and use them to catch prey.

Brittle star
Brittle stars are not starfish, but they are similar.

Spines
The spines catch animals in the water that flows past the star.

Arms and body
A brittle star uses its arms to feed and to walk. The disk in the center is its body.

FACT FILE

DIET
Fish, sea urchins, other starfish

HABITAT
Coral reefs and coastal waters

0	4 inches (10 cm)	8 inches (20 cm)

STARFISH
ASTEROIDEA

DEPTH

0 feet (0 m)

19,500 feet (6,000 m)

SIZE • 6 INCHES (15 CM)

ON THE OCEAN FLOOR

Near to land, the oceans are shallow and sunlight and warmth can reach the sea floor. The seabed here makes a good home for many animals. Farther out to sea, there is less light and the seafloor can be a dark, empty, and almost lifeless place.

GIANT TUBEWORM
RIFTIA PACHYPTILA

DEPTH

5,200 feet
(1,600 m)

19,500 feet
(7,000 m)

SIZE • UP TO 8 FEET (2.5 M)

Smoker
This is a place where super-hot water and minerals pour out from the ocean floor.

Tubeworms
Clusters of tubeworms grow around the smoker. The red body of a tubeworm pokes out of its long white tube.

Hydrophone records sound

SEA CUCUMBER

Sea cucumbers swallow mud and sand, and feed on bits of dead animals or plants within it. Some sea cucumbers graze on seaweed.

A red-lined sea cucumber crawling over the Great Barrier Reef.

Juvenile fish hide among the spines of this radiant sea urchin.

SEA URCHINS

The long spines of a sea urchin can deliver a painful dose of venom. These prickly animals mostly live in warm coastal places.

⊕ SEA SMOKERS

There are places on the seabed where hot water and minerals escape under the seabed. Strange animals, such as tubeworms, live here and feed on the minerals.

CHRISTMAS TREE WORM

Christmas tree worms are named after their beautiful spiral of colorful tentacles. They feed on plankton that they take out of the water.

Probe measures levels of hydrogen

FEATHER STAR

Feather stars are also called sea lilies and they are a type of echinoderm, not a plant. Long feathery arms surround the feather star's mouth and are held up, into the water. These arms, or tentacles, capture plankton in the water and move it toward the animal's mouth.

GLOSSARY

APHOTIC ZONE
The part of the ocean beneath the Photic Zone, which stretches down to a depth of about 650 feet (200 m). No light reaches down to the Aphotic Zone.

BALEEN
Plates made of keratin inside the mouths of whales such as humpback whales and blue whales. The whales use the baleen plates to filter small fish and krill from the water.

BLOWHOLE
A hole at the top of the heads of whales and dolphins. The animals only breathe through their blowholes, not through their mouths.

BONY FISH
Fish whose skeleton is made from bone rather than from cartilage.

BREACHING
When an animal leaps out of the water completely. Some sharks breach to catch prey, while scientists are unsure why some whales and dolphins breach. They may be trying to get rid of parasites or just showing off.

CARAPACE
The tough upper shell found on crabs, turtles, spiders, and other arachnids.

CARTILAGE
A flexible substance found in some of our joints and in our ears and noses. A shark's whole skeleton is made of cartilage.

FINS
Flaps on the sides of sea creatures such as fish and whales, which they use to swim.

FISH
Animals that live in water and breathe using gills. Fish use muscles attached to their backbones and fins to move their bodies in an "S" shape.

FLIPPERS
Limbs of some sea-going animals that are used for swimming. In penguins, the wings have adapted to become flippers. In turtles and seals, the flippers are their modified arms and legs.

FLUKES
The horizontal parts of a whale's tail. They are moved up and down to push the whale through the water.

GILL
A body part in fish and some amphibians that allows them to breathe underwater. The gills take in oxygen that is dissolved in the water.

HATCHLING
The name given to a young reptile or bird that has just hatched out of its shell.

INVERTEBRATE
An animal that does not have a backbone. Most animals are invertebrates. Some of these have a hard outer exoskeleton, while others have bodies that are completely soft.

KRILL

Small shrimplike creatures that are found in large numbers in the oceans. Krill are the main food of many fish, squid, and whales.

LARVAE

The young of animals such as fish, insects, and amphibians. The larvae often look completely different from the adults, and can live in very different parts of the ocean.

LURE

The long, thin fin found on the heads of anglerfish. A lure is used attract a prey.

MIGRATION

Going on a long journey in search of food or a good place to breed and raise young.

PHOTIC ZONE

The uppermost part of the ocean, down to a depth of about 650 feet (200 m), where light can reach.

PHOTOPHORE

The light-making organs found on some fish and other creatures that glow in the dark.

PLANKTON

The name given to tiny microscopic living things found in the ocean. There are two types of plankton—phytoplankton, which is made up of miniature plants, and zooplankton, which consists of tiny animals.

POD

The name given to a group of whales or dolphins.

REPTILE

A group of animals that have scaly skin and lay eggs. Reptiles are cold-blooded, which means they cannot keep their body temperature constant. Crocodiles, turtles, and lizards are all reptiles.

SCALES

Small protective plates that form part of the outer skin of some animals. Fish have bony scales, while reptiles have scales made of keratin.

SPECIES

A kind of living thing. Members of the same species are very similar to one another and can breed and produce offspring.

SPERMACETI

A waxy substance found in the heads of whales. It may help a whale to float and it may also be used to produce sounds.

SPY HOPPING

The habit of poking a head above the water's surface to look for prey or predators. Spy hopping is performed by whales and some sharks.

SUBMERSIBLE

A miniature submarine designed to dive down to extreme depths. Submersibles can be robotic or they can carry people.

TUSK

An enlarged tooth that sticks out of an animal's mouth. Narwhals and walruses have tusks.

VENOM

A toxic substance that can cause a painful wound, or in the worst cases, paralysis and even death.

INDEX

79

ACKNOWLEDGMENTS

Picture credits

(t=top, b=bottom, l=left, r=right, c=center, fc=front cover)

123RF: Andreas Altenburger 59 bc

Corbis: © Dave Fleetham/Design Pics/Corbis 14 bl

FLPA: Frans Lanting/FLPA 9 tc, Hiroya Minakuchi/Minden Pictures/FLPA 9 br, 11 cr, 14 l, 29 r, 37 br, Fabien Michenet/Biosphoto/ FLPA 10-11 c, Tui De Roy/Minden Pictures/FLPA 10 bl, Norbert Wu/Minden Pictures/FLPA 14-15 c,17 cl, 26 tcl, 30 bl, 31 tr, 34 tr, 37 tr, 45 br, 55 br, 69 tr, 75 c, Chris & Tilde Stuart/FLPA 13 bc, 15 cr, Roger Tidman/FLPA 11 bc, 17 bc, Brandon Cole/Biosphoto/ FLPA 15 br, 37 bcr, Samuel Blanc/Biosphoto/FLPA 17 tc, Mark Sisson/FLPA 19 tc, Chris Stenger/Minden Pictures/FLPA 19 br, SA Team/FN/Minden/FLPA 20 tcl, Peter Reynolds/FLPA 20 bl, Reinhard Dirscherl/FLPA 22-23 c, 36 cl, 48-49 c, 51 cr, 66-67 c, Photo Researchers/FLPA 23 cl, 47 tc, 58-59 c, Flip Nicklin/Minden Pictures/FLPA 25 cl, 36 bl, Mike Parry/Minden Pictures/FLPA 25 br, Patricio Robles Gil/Minden Pictures/FLPA 28 c, Mathieu Pujol/Biosphoto/FLPA 29 bl, Imagebroker/FLPA 28 bl, 33 tr, 36 bcl, OceanPhoto/FLPA 33 br, Richard Herrmann/Minden Pictures/FLPA 36-37 c, 70-71 c, Fred Bavendam/Minden Pictures/FLPA 32 bl, 49 tr, 67 br, 75 br, IMAGEBROKER, NORBERT PROBST/Imagebroker/FLPA 32 bcl, 50-51 c, 72 bcl, 75 tr, 75 cr, Peter David/FLPA 46 c, D P Wilson/FLPA 48 tcl, 56 bc, 59 tr, 59 cr, Norbert Probst/Imagebroker/FLPA 49 tcr, Chris Newbert/Minden Pictures/FLPA 50 bcl, Colin Marshall/FLPA 51 bl, 70 cl, H. Eisenbeiss/FLPA 58 bl, Birgitte Wilms/Minden Pictures/FLPA 61 cr, Albert Lleal/ Minden Pictures/FLPA 27 r, 63 br, Manfred Bail/Imagebroker/FLPA 62 bl, Steve Trewhella/FLPA 62 br, Gerard Lacz/FLPA 63 tr, Colin Marshall/FLPA 66 cl, 67 cr, 70 cl, 70 bl, IMAGEBROKER, MICHAEL MOXTER/Imagebroker/FLPA 71 br

Getty: Gavin Parsons 18-19 c, Lisa Graham 18 bl, Brian J. Skerry 18 bc, Mauricio Handler 20 cl, Wolfgang Poelzer 22 bl, 27 tcr, Tobias Bernhard 22 cl, David Jenkins 24 cl, Jones/Shimlock-Secret Sea Visions 26-27 c

Naturepl: © DOC WHITE/naturepl.com 13 cr, © David Shale/naturepl.com 43 tr, © David Shale/naturepl.com 47 cr, © Visuals Unlimited/naturepl.com 60-61 c, © Solvin Zankl/naturepl.com 42 cl, © Jurgen Freund/naturepl.com 48 cl, © Franco Banfi/naturepl.com 30 br

Shutterstock: OlegD 62-63 c

SPL: Jeff Rotman/SCIENCE PHOTO LIBRARY 6 cl, ALEXIS ROSENFELD/SCIENCE PHOTO LIBRARY 6 bc, DAVID FLEETHAM, VISUALS UNLIMITED /SCIENCE PHOTO LIBRARY 66 bl, NOAA PMEL Vents Program/SCIENCE PHOTO LIBRARY 74 bl, SUSUMU NISHINAGA/SCIENCE PHOTO LIBRARY 50 bl

Superstock: Reinhard Dirscherl/age fotostock/SuperStock 13 tcl, age fotostock/SuperStock 28-29 c, 35 bc, Norbert Probst/imagebroker/imagebroker.net/SuperStock 32-33 c, Stuart Westmorland/Science Faction/SuperStock 35 tr, Minden Pictures/SuperStock 42 bl, BlueGreen Pictures/SuperStock 53 tr, Minden Pictures/SuperStock 72 lc